Vincent van Gogh's Cat

Written and illustrated by
Second Grade Students of
East Washington Academy
Muncie, Indiana

Scholastic Inc.
New York   Toronto   London   Auckland   Sydney   Mexico City   New Delhi   Hong Kong   Buenos Aires

Vincent van Gogh's cat
stepped out of a field of sunflowers,

tiptoed around a pond of water lilies,

explored an exotic jungle,

leaped across a purpled landscape,

twirled beneath the Tree of Life,

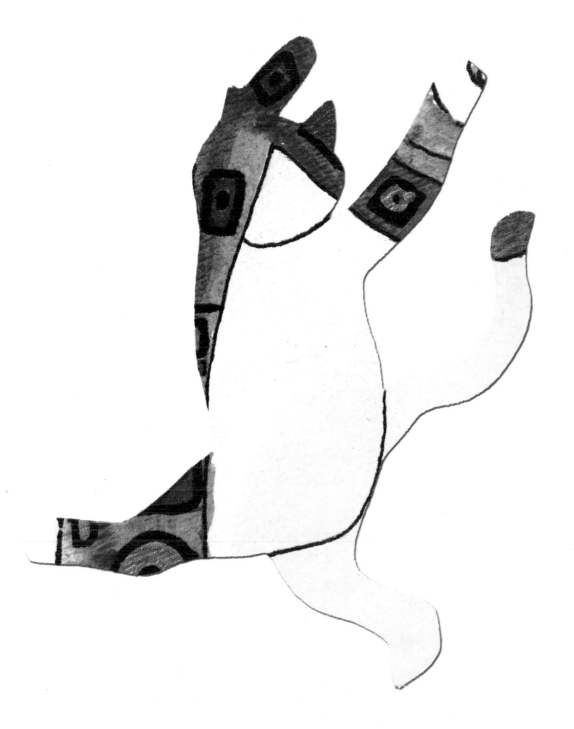

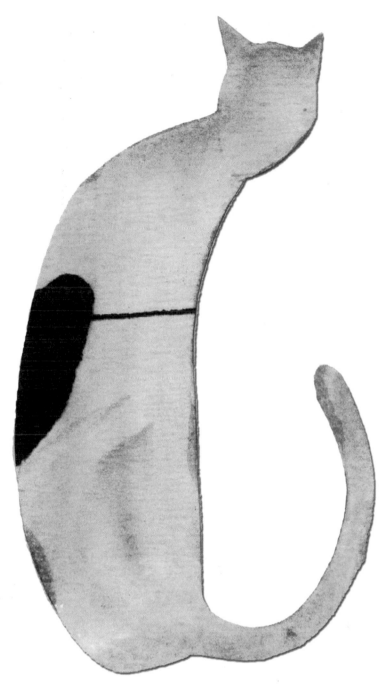

stretched beneath a flaming sun,

danced through a sea of green taffeta,

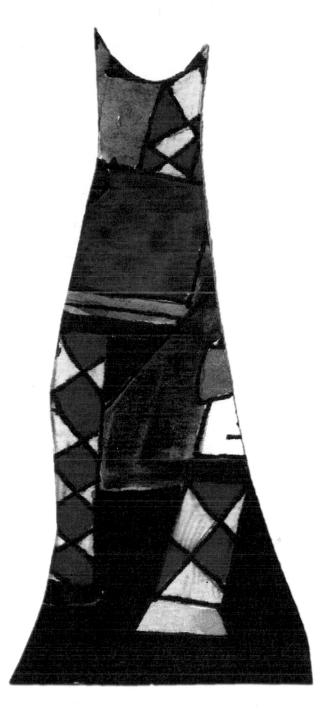

sang to the melody of three musicians,

reclined in an artist's moonlit studio,

napped near a child in a blue chair,

climbed a spiraling, starry stair,

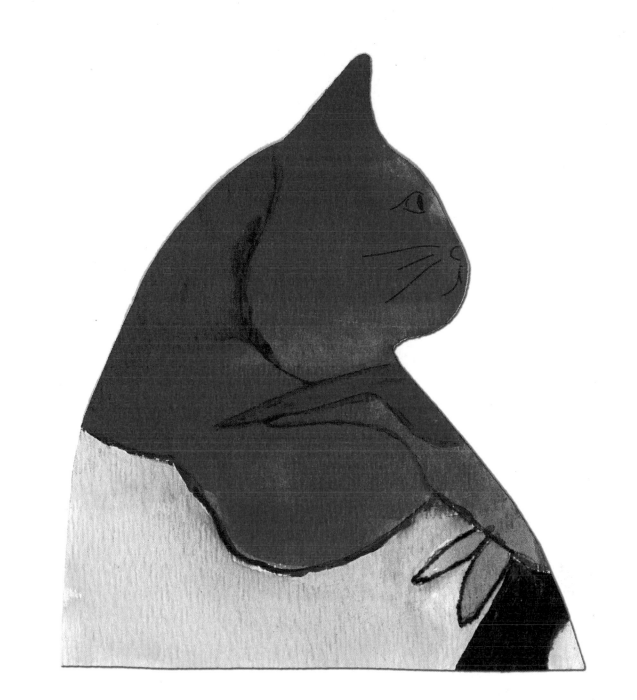

sniffed petals of a bright, red poppy,

basked in the warmth of a golden glow,

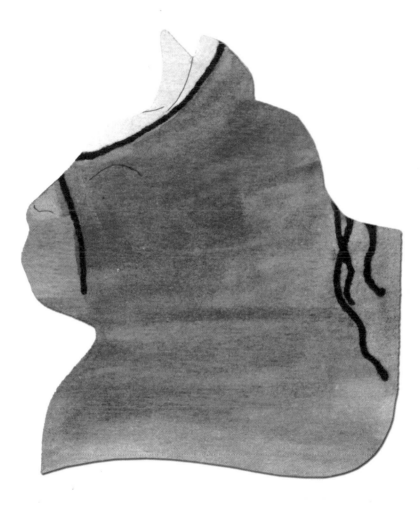

and waltzed into a
starry night!